Celebrate Onam With Me!

Shoumi Sen
Illustrated By Rudra Bose

To Baba and Ma ~ Shoumi

ISBN: 978-1-7354391-0-5

Onam is a 10-day harvest festival celebrated in Kerala, India. According to legend, the great King Mahabali visits Kerala every year and it is this homecoming that is celebrated as the festival of Onam.

It is harvest time in Kerala, we are here to celebrate
The festival of Onam, it's going to be great!
Hi, I'm Riya and am with my friend Unni this year
Let me tell you a story that you will want to hear!

There lived a famous demon king, Mahabali was his name.
His people loved him, but the gods grew jealous of his fame.
They went to Lord Vishnu, their hearts filled with fear
"Please do something," they begged, "or else our end is near."

Lord Vishnu went to Mahabali in the form of a little boy
He called himself Vamana, but this was a decoy
"How can I help you?" the king asked. The request was small.
"The land I can cover in three steps, that's all."

The boy grew like magic and took one giant step
With that, he covered the earth and the heavens with his next
Everyone was shocked and Mahabali now knew
This little boy was in fact, the great Lord Vishnu!

With nothing else to give, the king offered his head
Knowing he'd be sent to another world instead.
Before leaving for the underworld, he had one last request,
"Can I see my people once a year?" Lord Vishnu said "Yes!"

In Kerala or beyond, wherever we may roam,
We come together on Onam; our king is coming home!
In the month of Chingam at Unni's house this year
Everyone has gathered for ten days of fun and cheer.

A beautiful flower pookalam our aunty has planned
Unni and I run over to lend a helping hand
"We win first prize each year", says Aunty with a smile
"Lots of planning and hard work, but it's all worthwhile!"

Brand new clothes for everyone,
a pavada for me to wear
We've spent the whole day shopping,
there's excitement in the air!

Look at those enormous snake boats, it's Vallamkali today,
Hundreds of expert oarsmen singing and rowing away
But even more surprising are the crowds that gather here
Hundreds, no, thousands, have come to clap and cheer!

Ladies in lovely saris,
Kaikottikali they perform
With the lamp in the middle,
with its glow so warm

We've been up since sunrise, it's Thiruvonam today.
We have offered our prayers; "Onashamsakal" we say.

The pookalams in town are amazing, but 1st prize we win
"The competition was intense!" says Aunty with a grin

Ever since this morning, in the kitchen we have been
Making the Onasadya, a meal fit for our king
So many veggies, more arrive by the bunch,
I'm amazed that all of this will be ready for lunch!

Look at all the dishes, what a sight to behold
Placed on a banana leaf, twenty-six, I'm told
Each item has its spot, Unni tells me as we serve,
Payasam, sambar, avial, all placed along a curve

Everyone has eaten, the gift giving has begun
Ammama showers presents that we open one by one.
In my brand new pavada, a festive tune I hum
Let's get together every year and celebrate Onam!

Onam Dictionary

Ammama (Um-mum-ma)

Maternal grandmother in Malayalam.

Avial (Uh-vee-yal)

Avial or Aviyal is a traditional dish that is served during Onam Sadya. It is a thick mixture of vegetables and coconut, seasoned with coconut oil and curry leaves.

Chingam (Ching-um)

Onam is celebrated during Chingam, the first month of the traditional Malayalam calendar. It corresponds with either August or September.

Kaikottikali (Kai-ko-tee-kuh-lee)

This is an elegant dance peformed during Onam. (kai=hand, koti=clap, kali=play). Ladies dance in a circle around a lamp, while singing songs and clapping. Other dances from Kerala are Kathakali and Mohiniyattam.

Onam (O-num)

Onam is a 10 day long harvest festival in Kerala celebrated to mark the annual visit of King Mahabali to his land. People decorate their homes, make a lot of delicious food and take part in many cultural activities as we have seen in this book.

Kerala (Kay-rah-lah)

Often called 'God's own country', Kerala is a state in the southern part of India, where Onam is celebrated. People of Kerala are called Malayalis and they speak Malayalam (Muh-luh-yaa-lum).

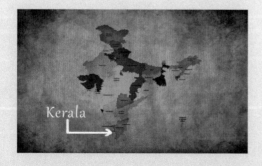

Kerala

FUN FACT: Did you know that the word Malayalam is a palindrome?

A palindrome is a word that reads the same from left to right as well as right to left.

Onam Dictionary

Onashamsakal (O-naa-shum-sah-kal)

Onashamsakal is what we say to greet each other during Onam (ashamsakal=wishes).

Onasadya (O-na-sadh-ya)

Sadya means banquet. Onasadya is the traditional vegetarian feast served on Thiruvonam, the most important day of Onam. Served on a banana leaf, it can contain 20-40 items.

Pavada (Paa-va-da)

A pavada is a brightly colored, long skirt worn by girls, typically made of silk. During Onam, girls wear a traditional skirt and blouse outfit, called 'pattu pavada'. Women wear white sarees with a gold border. Men wear a traditional outfit called a 'mundu' with a shirt.

Payasam (Paa-ya-sum)

A yummy traditional rice pudding served as a dessert in the Onasadya.

Pookalam (Poo-ku-lam)

A pookalam (Poo=flower, kalam=artwork) is an intricate, colorful arrangement of flowers on the floor. During Onam, families decorate the entrances of their homes with beautiful pookalams to welcome King Mahabali.

Pulikali (Pu-lee-ka-lee)

Pulikali (puli=tiger, kali=play) is a traditional folk dance performed during Onam. It is a 'tiger dance' in which adults and children dress up as tigers and dance to the accompaniment of drums.

Onam Dictionary

Sambar (Saam-baar)

This is a delicious lentil and vegetable stew, popular in southern India and part of the Onasadya feast. The addition of tamarind gives it a distinctive taste.

Thiruvonam (Thee-rue-voh-num)

Thiruvonam or Thiru Onam means 'sacred Onam day' and refers to the 10th and most important day of the Onam festival. Mahabali is said to visit Kerala on Thiruvonam and everyone dresses up in their best clothes to welcome him.

Vallamkali (Va-llum-kuh-lee)

Vallamkali (vallam=boat, kali=play) refers to the traditional snake boat races that are held in Kerala during Onam. Beautifully decorated boats, sometimes over 100 feet long, take part in these races, with oarsmen rowing in perfect rhythm to boat songs. These races are extremely popular and draw crowds in the thousands.

FUN FACT: Kerala has a huge number of coconut plantations. (kera=coconut tree, alam=land). Kerala can be thought to be the land of coconut trees.

About the Author

Shoumi Sen is the creator of 'From The Toddler Diaries', a series of children's books on Indian culture and mythology, which began as a series of poems that she wrote for her daughter. This collection was the life of several bedtime story sessions and play dates with friends. Inspired by this interest among kids and encouraged by their parents, she decided to publish the collection. Shoumi is a Strategy, Sales and Marketing professional at a leading global energy management company and lives in Los Angeles with her husband and daughter.

Visit Shoumi's website: www.shoumisen.com

Facebook: https://www.facebook.com/FromTheToddlerDiaries

Instagram: @fromthetoddlerdiariesbooks

Acknowledgements

Thank you to Sapna, for the late nights and long conversations; without you this book would not be complete.

To Deepti, for telling me the story of Mahabali when we were kids. To Sandhya, for always being there.

Books in the Series

Celebrate
Holi With Me!

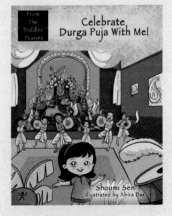

Celebrate
Durga Puja With Me!

Celebrate
Onam With Me!

86625822R00024